Biological Science

Hands-On Activities to Promote Student Involvement

by
Frank White

illustrated by Veronica Terrill

Cover by Ted Warren

Copyright © 1993, Good Apple

Good Apple
1204 Buchanan St., Box 299
Carthage, IL 62321-0299

SIMON & SCHUSTER *A Paramount Communications Company*

Dedication

*Among the three or four million cradles now rocking in the land
are some which this nation would preserve for ages as sacred things, if we could know
which ones they are.*

Mark Twain

Dedicated to those kids who ask, "Why?"

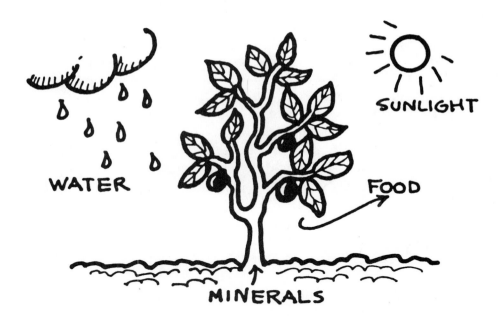

Table of Contents

GA1443

Preface

This book is designed to put science investigation in the hands of the students. Learning becomes more concrete and concepts mastered more fully when learning is interactive. *Science* means "experimentation," and it should be kept in mind that the manipulation of materials with a goal is as important at this stage of scientific investigation as a "successful" outcome.

The book has been divided into teacher background information and projects. The projects are further divided into student projects and teacher/student projects. The student projects are designed as class-wide projects, and it is suggested that students be allowed to work together in small groups of three or four. Some student projects are designed to be completed at home and returned the following day.

The teacher/student projects are designed to be completed by the teacher with student help and input. The tendency to "do" for the students should be avoided. At every opportunity let the students measure, pour, mix, categorize, taste, cut, tie, weigh, and most of all discuss and be led to ask questions about the projects. The opportunity for in-depth, scientific understanding and appreciation exists within these pages, but only your enthusiasm and interest can bring science to life.

Science often requires more different kinds of materials than any other subject area. While an effort was made to keep the material requirements to a minimum, certain materials are musts. The teacher should feel free to make substitutions if necessary. As an example, a large glass jar may work instead of an expensive aquarium.

Have the students play an active role in supplying the necessary materials for projects. When the students bring in science supplies, they are providing more than the materials; they are coming to class prepared with a positive attitude about "their" science projects.

A positive attitude and genuine interest will pay far greater dividends in a child's education than learning a given scientific fact. A fact may provide a specific answer, but attitude, interest and an inquiring mind will provide the questions...and questions are the driving force in science.

GA1443

Biological Sciences–Plants

Plants are living organisms. Because their growth is usually slow and they don't move around on their own, children don't think of plants as living in the same way as they do dogs, cats, fish, or birds. It is important that children learn that plants are at the bottom of the food chain and that all animal life depends on plants. All animals, including man with all his technology and sophistication, cannot do something the lowly radish can do–make its own food. This process of food production is called photosynthesis.

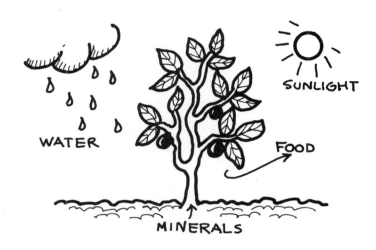

Growing Plants in the Classroom
In addition to the regular potted plants that spruce up a classroom, several simple plant-growing experiments can help bring a better understanding of plants in a graphic way.

The lowly sweet potato is a simple plant to grow and gives the students an excellent opportunity to study plant growth.
(Student Project 1)

Student Project 1

1

GA1443

Tropism, an orientation or movement as a response to a stimuli, is another plant study that can be made in the classroom. Geotropism and seed germination will interest the student and lead to the realization that roots react downward to the force of gravity and plants grow upward.

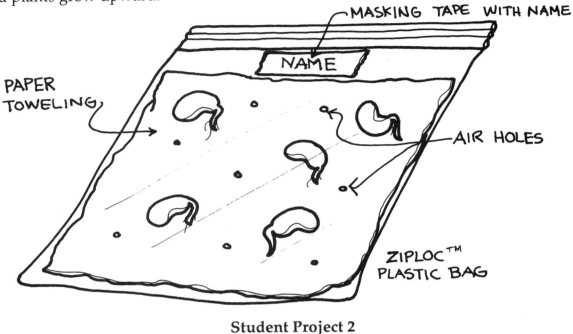

Student Project 2

Further study of tropism can include phototropism (Student Project 3) and hydrotropism (Student Project 4). Students should be able to observe that several forces are at work in determining the growth of the plant.

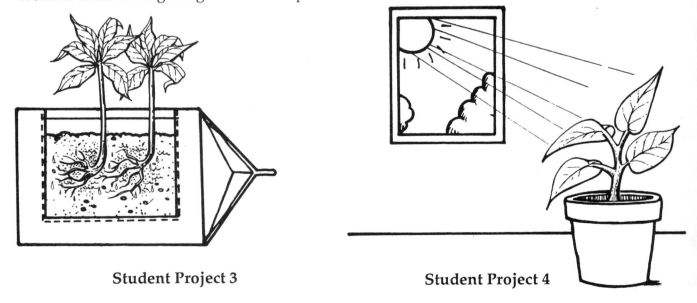

Student Project 3

Milk container demonstrating hydrotropism

Student Project 4

Leaves facing window or light demonstrate phototropism.

Once the seeds are germinated (Student Project 2), an excellent lesson for the students is viewing the developing seed with a biocular microscope or strong hand lens (Student Project 5). A study of the fragile root hairs will lead students to understanding that minerals, which are too small to be seen, are absorbed by the root hairs and help the plants to grow.

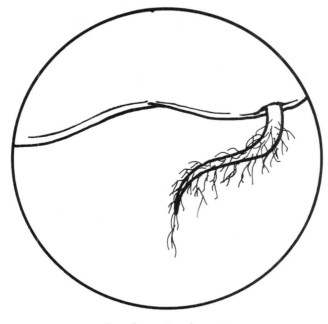

Student Project 5

To give evidence of the need for nutrients, grow some of the germinated seeds in sterile play sand and some in potting soil (Student Project 6). All these projects go together to show that plants are complex organisms requiring sunlight, water, and nutrients to grow and are affected by many different forces.

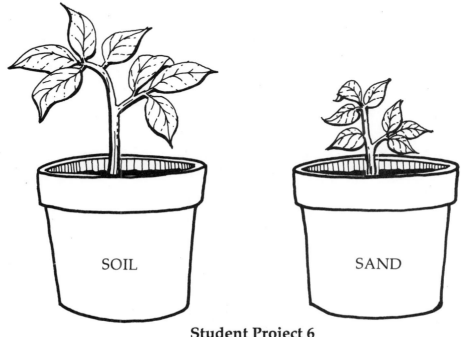

Student Project 6

GA1443

Geranium Geotropism

Teacher/Student Project 1

This experiment demonstrates geotropism. Use three geraniums or other hardy, fast-growing plants already potted. Have the students note the orientation of the plant. A good follow-up discussion question is "Can plants move?" Some students may point out that by "spreading out" vines, plants are also able to move from place to place.

This project will take several weeks to complete; however students will clearly see that stems respond negatively to gravity, growing away from its pull.

4

Growing a Sweet Potato Plant

Student Project 1

The sweet potato is a fun and easy plant to grow. For this project you will need three toothpicks, a glass or jar, a sweet potato, and water. Fill the jar about three-fourths full of water being sure to leave enough room so it won't overflow when you put in the sweet potato. Next, holding the sweet potato vertically, insert the toothpicks. The toothpicks should be evenly spaced into the sweet potato so that when it is placed in the jar, the sweet potato will sit half in and half out of the water. Check your sweet potato's water level daily. After leaves appear, use a spray bottle and give your plant a "shower" twice a week to remove dust and control pests. Draw pictures in the boxes below to record your plant's growth.

1 Day   1 Week   1 Month

There are over 350,000 different species of plants.

Which Way Do They Grow?

Student Project 2

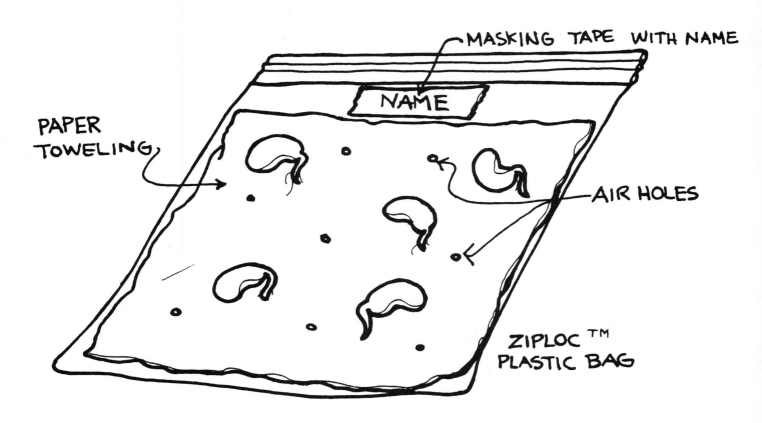

MASKING TAPE WITH NAME

NAME

PAPER TOWELING

AIR HOLES

ZIPLOC ™ PLASTIC BAG

Seeds seem to know which way is down and this experiment will show it. Poke several air holes in a plastic Ziploc™ bag. (Be careful and don't poke yourself.) Place two folded paper towels in the bag. Put six to eight seeds between the toweling and the bag (green bean, lima bean, corn, and radish seeds work well), and add enough water to dampen the towel. The bag should not drip water but should be damp. Put your name on a piece of masking tape and tape it to your bag. Staple your bag to a bulletin board. Check your bag daily and add water if it starts to dry out. Observe the direction of the roots as the seeds start to germinate (grow). Did the roots all grow the same direction? _____ What direction? _____

After two weeks, rotate the bag 90 degrees ($\frac{1}{4}$ turn) so the opening is on the side. Observe the roots for several days with the bag in the new position. Did the roots continue to grow in the same direction? _____ If they grew in a new direction, what was it?_____ What can you say about the direction plant roots grow?

_____

_____

_____

_____

Your germinated seeds should be saved for use in later projects.

Some coconut seeds can weigh up to twenty pounds.

GA1443

Plants Need Water

Student Project 3

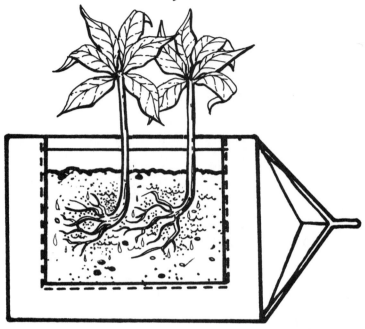

For a plant to grow it needs water, sunlight, and nutrients. This experiment will demonstrate how plants seek out water. Have an adult cut out two adjacent sides of a clean, half-gallon milk carton. Slip in a piece of clear glass to replace one side. Poke several small drainage holes in the bottom of the carton and spread a thin layer of gravel on the bottom. Fill the carton with potting soil and carefully transplant your seeds from Project 2. Place the plants near the glass so you can see the roots grow. Very lightly water only one end of the carton and note the results. Keeping the glass covered when not observing the roots will stimulate root growth. After two weeks, what happened to the seeds near the area you watered?

_____

What happened to the seeds farthest from the area you watered?

_____

The seeds of the tobacco plant are so small that 2500 can fit in a $3/4$ " seed pouch.

8

Giving Plants a Turn–Phototropism

Student Project 4

If you have a houseplant in your home, first notice how the leaves face a window. They are facing light–one of the three needs plants have to remain healthy. With a parent's help, rotate the plant one-half turn and notice how many of the leaves are "facing away" from the window. Observe daily your houseplant and see if it slowly "turns" back toward the light.

The oldest living things, bristlecone pines, are over 4000 years old.

GA1443

If Plants Have Root Hairs, Do They Ever Need Haircuts?

Student Project 5

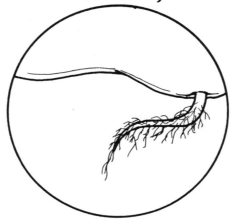

Use a hand lens or microscope to observe the root hairs on your germinating seeds (Student Project 2). Besides anchoring the plant in place, the roots provide a passageway for water and minerals to move into the plant. The nutrients a plant needs to grow are too small to be seen with even a microscope. Using your hand lens or microscope, draw what your seed's root hairs look like in the hand lens below.

The largest living plants are the giant sequoia trees of California. General Sherman, the largest sequoia, contains enough lumber to build 200 homes.

Plants Need Nutrients to Grow

Student Project 6

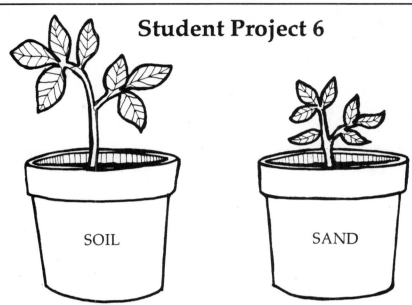

SOIL   SAND

With an adult's help, poke several small holes in the bottom of two paper cups. Fill one cup two-thirds full of potting soil and fill the other cup two-thirds full of sterile sand. Carefully transplant one of your germinating seeds into each cup and water every other day. The potting soil contains nutrients the plant needs to grow. The sand is a nutrient-poor environment, and you should be able to see a difference in how fast each plant grows. Use the chart below to record the results of your experiment.

Day No.		Plant Condition			Height of Plant	Day No.		Plant Condition			Height of Plant
		Good	Fair	Poor				Good	Fair	Poor	
	Plant A						Plant A				
	Plant B						Plant B				
	Plant A						Plant A				
	Plant B						Plant B				
	Plant A						Plant A				
	Plant B						Plant B				
	Plant A										
	Plant B										

Seven hundred kinds of poisonous plants grow in the United States. A single seed from the rosary pea plant can kill a person.

GA1443

Leaves are the main food-producing structure of a plant. A simple analogy for students can be that leaves act as a "factory" where carbon dioxide, light, and water are made into food. Comparing a banana leaf (if one is available) to a more common flower leaf or blade of grass will demonstrate nature's variation in leaf production. The Gunnera leaf from South America looks like a giant umbrella with a diameter of over eight feet! A leaf collage can be a great class project to demonstrate leaf variety.

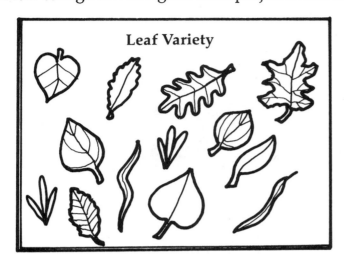

Leaf Variety

Student Project 7

A large piece of butcher paper on a bulletin board is a good place to display the students' leaf collage.

Inside a leaf the green substance, chlorophyll, uses light, water, and carbon dioxide to produce simple sugar compounds. This process is a complicated reaction of electron transfer at the molecular level. The process is called photosynthesis. To demonstrate the importance of light in the reaction, the students can perform a nifty experiment with paper circles, paper clips, and living plants.

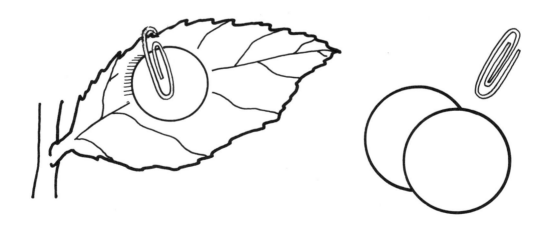

Student Project 8

A fun and interesting student project can be done making leaf transfers.

Student Project 9

Another simpler art project uses the "leaf rubbings" with the side of a crayon. A leaf art collage is a fine way to study the veins of leaves.

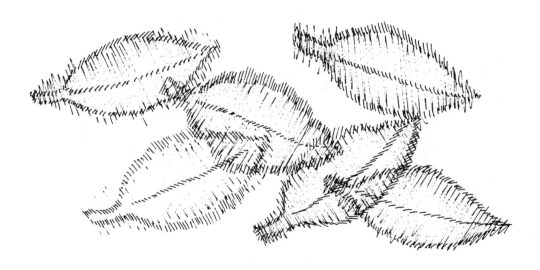

Student Project 10

Leaf Collage

Student Project 7

A "tree detective" can identify a tree by its leaves. Each tree's leaves are particular to size, shape, color, design, and arrangement. Your job is to collect leaves from as many different plants as possible. Try to identify each plant from which you take leaves. Remember needles from pine trees, blades of grass, and cactus spines are all leaves. Also, try to collect as many different types of leaves as possible to place on your class' leaf collage.

Olive leaves represent peace and hope.
Laurel leaves symbolize victory. "Laurels"
Oak leaves stand for glory, honor, and strength.

14

Leaves Need Light

Student Project 8

Water, air, and sunlight are the important raw materials for a leaf's food factory. A leaf makes food from the air and water if chlorophyll (the green substance on plants) is activated by sunlight. You can perform an interesting experiment that demonstrates a plant's need for light to grow and produce chlorophyll.

1. From a piece of construction paper or thin cardboard, cut out two circles about an inch (2.54 cm) in diameter.

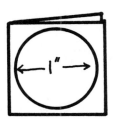 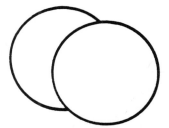

2. Use paper clips to secure these two circles to a green, growing leaf.

TOP AND BOTTOM

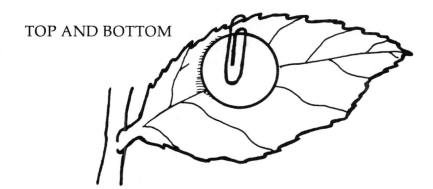

3. After three or four days, remove the paper circles. Observe the round, light-colored patch on the leaf. This is the result of chlorophyll production being stopped due to lack of sunlight. Draw an illustration of the results of your experiment.

The sapodilla tree of tropical America produces the chicle used to make chewing gum.

GA1443

Name _____

Date _____

Leaf Diversity

Student Project 9

Nature creates leaves of many sizes, colors, and shapes. An interesting and beautiful art project can be done using leaves, construction paper, crayons, and a hot iron. (Always make sure an adult supervises the iron to avoid burns.)

Materials:
>2 pieces light-colored construction paper
>5-6 soft, pliable leaves
>crayons
>a hot iron

Procedure:
1. Rub one side of a leaf with a crayon. Cover the entire surface of *one side*. Use care not to tear the leaf.

2. Place the leaf, crayon-side down, on a piece of light-colored construction paper. Cover the leaf with another piece of construction paper and carefully press down on the area with a hot iron.

3. The hot wax will make an image of the leaf on the paper.

The leaf is the main food-producing structure of a plant.

Leaf Art Collage

Student Project 10

You can create a beautiful leaf art collage by making several leaf rubbings using construction paper and crayons. Here's how.

Place a large leaf under a sheet of white tissue paper. Use the side of a crayon and rub the tissue paper until a leaf design appears.

Reposition the leaf, change colors and repeat the procedure. Repeat the procedure several times until you've created your leaf art collage.

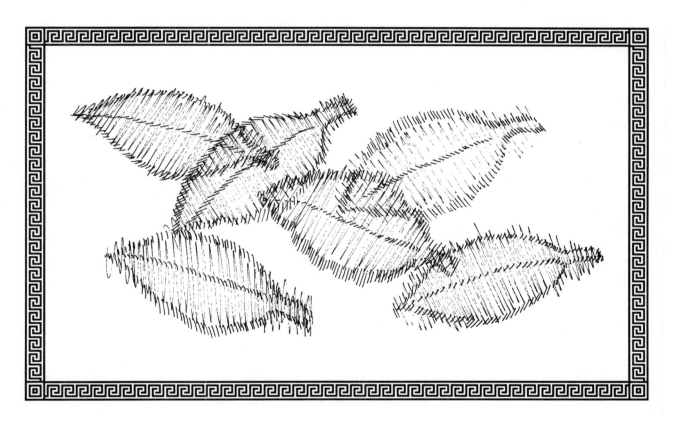

Frame your project with bright construction paper and presto—a beautiful leaf art collage.

The African raffia palms have leaves up to fifty feet long.

Water is one of the important life-sustaining requirements of a plant. Most water is absorbed by a plant's roots and transported to the leaves by the plant's stem. The cells that carry water are called the xylem tissue of the plant. Cells that transport food form the plant's phloem tissue. Water transport in a plant can be observed easily with the use of food coloring or ink and a fresh cut flower (a white carnation works great). A stalk of celery with the leaves attached also will work well.

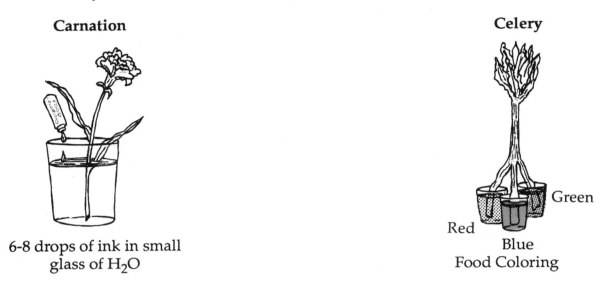

Carnation

6-8 drops of ink in small glass of H_2O

Celery

Green

Red

Blue
Food Coloring

Teacher/Student Project 2

Plants transpire water vapor through their leaves and stems. Plants help us by generating oxygen in our environment. To observe water vapor that plants give off, you can perform a simple experiment. Simply place a clear plastic bag over a growing green plant (perhaps the potted plant from Teacher/Student Project 1). Tie the bag securely with a twist tie around the stem and note how the water vapor transpired from the plant condenses on the inside of the bag.

Teacher/Student Project 3

18

GA1443

Plants are composed of many different kinds of cells. Most cells are so small a microscope is needed to view them. One of the best cells to view are those of the onion. The skin of the onion can be carefully peeled away and will provide a great view of a cell of a plant.

Student Project 11

Flowering plants reproduce by a process called pollination. A plant's male reproductive organs are called stamens. At the tip of the stamens are enlarged areas called anthers. Pollen is produced in this area. The female reproductive organ is called the pistil. It is composed of the stigma, style, and ovary of the plant. Fertilization takes place when pollen grains reach the stigma, travel down the style and reach the ovary. The fertilized egg develops into a seed containing the embryo. When the seed falls to the ground, moisture causes the seed coat to swell open and the embryo grows into a new plant.

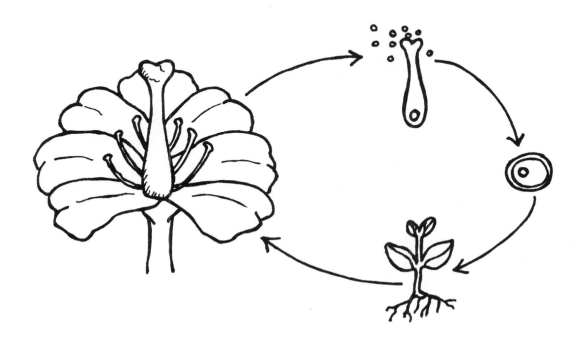

Student Project 12

Microscope slides can be made very easily from transparent tape, cut-up note cards, and an object you wish to observe.

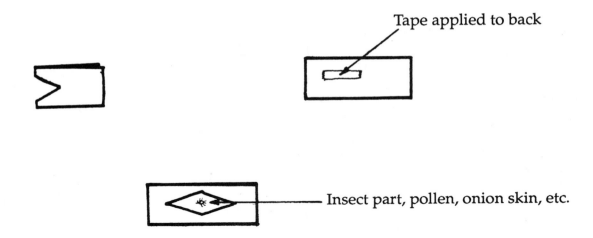

Tape applied to back

Insect part, pollen, onion skin, etc.

Student Project 13

These slides should be marked and covered with another clear strip of tape if you want to preserve them. A class collection of different slides makes an interesting and educational center. Try a microscope center with the materials laid out and the student information and direction sheet available. Let each student put his name on his slide and compare results. Compile a slide box of students' slides for investigation and comparison.

20

Water Transport in Plants

Teacher/Student Project 2

Plants need water to grow. After absorbing water through their roots, plants transport water in the xylem tissue of their stems. We can observe this water transport with the aid of a carnation or stalk of celery.

Materials:

    flower (carnation or similar)
    celery with leaves
    ink or food coloring

Carnation–Make a fresh, clean cut at the base of the stem of the flower. Place the stem in a glass with water. Add 8-10 drops of ink or food coloring (Figure 1).

Celery–Make a clean cut at the bottom of the celery stalk and carefully make three cuts laterally along the stalk. Place each stalk section in a glass of water with 8-10 drops of ink or food coloring (Figure 2).

Figure 1

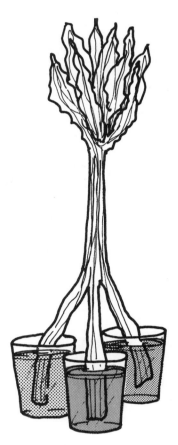

Figure 2

GA1443

Plant Transpiration

Teacher/Student Project 3

Plants transpire (give off) water vapor as they grow. It is possible to observe this process by "bagging" a living plant. Obtain a clear plastic bag and place it over the plant. Secure the bag with a twist tie or piece of string so the bag is airtight. Continue to water the plant as usual and note the results.

GA1443

Name _____

Date _____

Observing the Cell

Student Project 11

Cells are the basic unit of all living organisms. Plants are composed of cells. Some plants, such as algae, have only one cell while others, such as the giant redwood tree, are made up of millions of cells. Most cells are so small they can only be seen with a microscope. A thin covering, called the cell wall, encloses each cell. Inside the cell wall is a jelly-like substance called cytoplasm. The cytoplasm contains many different tiny structures. One such structure located in the cell's cytoplasm is the nucleus. The cell's nucleus controls everything the cell does. Let's take a look inside a cell and see what a plant cell looks like.

Materials:

white onion   tweezers
microscope slide   iodine or food coloring

Procedure:

Carefully peel the onion until you have a single layer of onion skin about the size of a dime. Place the skin on a microscope slide and add one drop of food coloring or iodine. This will stain the cells so they are easier to see under the microscope.

Observe the skin under the microscope and note your results.

In the circle below, draw a picture of the onion cells. Include the nucleus.

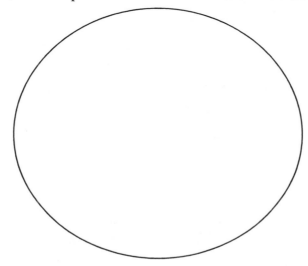

GA1443

Life Cycle of a Flowering Plant

Student Project 12

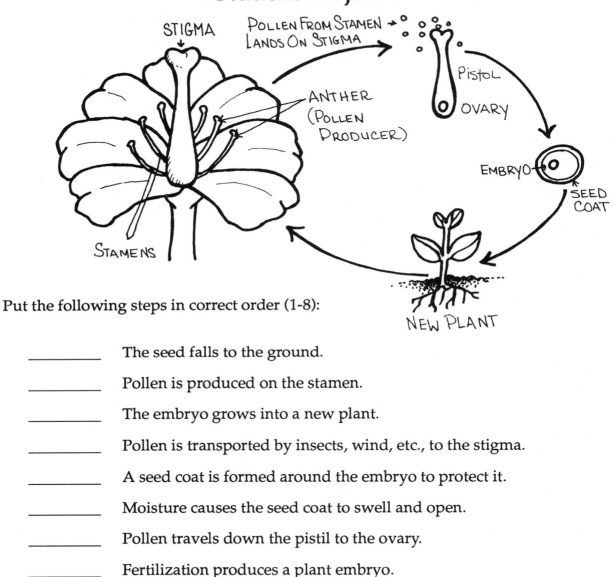

Put the following steps in correct order (1-8):

_____ The seed falls to the ground.

_____ Pollen is produced on the stamen.

_____ The embryo grows into a new plant.

_____ Pollen is transported by insects, wind, etc., to the stigma.

_____ A seed coat is formed around the embryo to protect it.

_____ Moisture causes the seed coat to swell and open.

_____ Pollen travels down the pistil to the ovary.

_____ Fertilization produces a plant embryo.

Licorice flavoring comes from the long sweet roots of the licorice plant, native to southern Europe.

GA1443

Making Microscope Slides

Student Project 13

It is always interesting to look closely at an otherwise common object under a microscope. It's fun to make your own microscope slide and amazingly easy to do.

Materials:

pair of scissors   index card
clear tape   small object to investigate

Procedure:

1. Cut the index card into strips approximately 1" (2.54 cm) wide and 4" (10.16 cm) long.

2. Fold the strip in half long. and make a triangular cut about $1/2$" (1.25 cm)

3. Open the strip and place a piece of tape over the center opening (sticky side toward the paper).

4. Place the object you wish to observe (dust particle, dead insect part, hair, piece of thread, etc.) on the tape.

5. Observe under a microscope.

The microscope was invented by Anton van Leeuwenhoek about 1590.

Yeasts are the simplest kinds of plants. They belong to the group of plants called fungi. Yeasts are important in the way they get their food. While each cell is growing, it produces enzymes. These enzymes can cause the starch in flour to change to sugar. The sugar is changed to alcohol and carbon dioxide. In bread making, the bubbles of carbon dioxide (CO_2) cause the bread to rise. The baking process evaporates the alcohol. To demonstrate the production of carbon dioxide, a simple experiment can be done.

Teacher/Student Project 4

The starch found in flour and a potato can be tested in a simple way. Iodine has become the standard test for the presence of starch. The presence of starch will turn reddish-brown iodine a dark blue-black.

A fun project can be the testing of various foods for the presence of starch.

Food	Reaction
Potato Chip	
Lifesaver	
Milk	
Soda Pop	
Bread	
Apple Slice	
Cornstarch	
Sugar	
Cracker	

Student Project 14

GA1443

Interesting to study while discussing the starch content of food is the effect of saliva on a cracker. A plain, unsalted soda cracker, if allowed to dissolve for several minutes in the mouth, will start to taste sweet as the enzyme *ptyalin* in saliva reacts with the starch in the cracker to produce a sugar called maltose.

Student Project 15

To further investigate foods and to amaze the students, demonstrate the effect of smell on taste. A person's tongue is only able to taste sweet, sour, bitter, and salty. Various combinations of these basic tastes with the olfactory apparatus (nose) give us all the variety of tastes we experience. If a person holds his nose, thus nullifying the effect of the olfactory system, it is impossible to distinguish between the taste of potatoes, apples, and onions. Make sure students are blindfolded so they can't see which food is selected for tasting.

potato   apple   onion

Teacher/Student Project 5

Color as well as taste has an effect on how we perceive a food will taste. Some simple food colorings added to regular and chocolate-flavored milk, orange and grapefruit juice, and plain water can create some comical realizations about how we "taste" foods with our eyes.

green milk   black orange juice

Teacher/Student Project 6

27   GA1443

If you have a magic store in your town, visit it and purchase some flash paper. It's a terrific starter for a number of science ideas and almost guaranteed to make your class come alive with questions and amazement. The flash paper combines with oxygen in the air to produce heat, light, and gases with no ash and at a very rapid speed. Normal paper burns at about 450° Fahrenheit. (The book *Fahrenheit 451* is about book burning.) Other materials have different temperatures at which they will combust or burn. The idea that citric acid will oxidize or "burn" at a lower temperature than paper can be used to make a very interesting project for the students. Magic writing will appear under the heat of a light bulb because the dry lemon juice burns at a lower temperature than the paper.

Student Project 16

Nature produces a variety of colors in the plant and animal world. Flowers come in almost all of the colors of the rainbow, while most leaves are varying shades of green. An interesting study of the pigments in plants can be performed with alcohol and white construction paper.

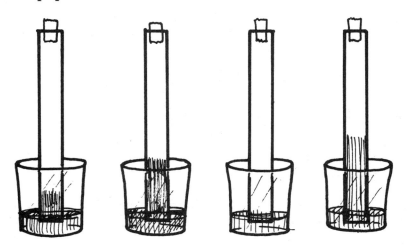

Student Project 17

GA1443

As a way to brighten up and make your classroom come alive, try having your class make terrariums. The students can probably help provide potting soil, charcoal, pebbles, and plants to help defray costs. A parent letter requesting help with materials is included and may be used if desired.

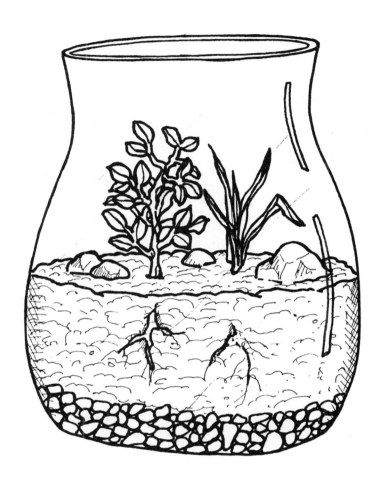

Student Project 18

29

GA1443

Carbon Dioxide Production

Teacher/Student Project 4

Yeasts are very small, one-celled plants. They are important for the fermentation process and are necessary to make bread rise.

Bread rises because of the production of carbon dioxide (CO_2). As carbon dioxide is produced, thousands of small bubbles are produced, causing the bread to become less dense, to expand, and to "rise."

The following experiment demonstrates CO_2 production by yeast.

Materials:

small soda pop bottle
3 tablespoons (45 ml) of flour
bottle half full of very warm
   (not hot) water

1 package of dry yeast
3 tablespoons (45 ml) of sugar
balloon to fit over mouth of bottle

Procedure:

To the bottle half filled with very warm water, add flour, yeast, and sugar. Mix thoroughly and place a balloon over the mouth of the bottle. Observe the results.

The gas that is produced to inflate the balloon is the CO_2 produced by the yeast.

An interesting follow-up to this experiment is to inflate a balloon to the same size as the yeast-inflated balloon. When dropped at the same time, the CO_2-filled balloon will fall faster. It is important to point out to the students that gravity pulls equally on all objects, but they fall at different rates because of air resistance and buoyancy. (A crumpled piece of paper vs. an uncrumpled piece of paper will fall at different rates.) CO_2 molecules are heavier than nitrogen molecules of which approximately 80 percent of our atmosphere is composed. Make sure students understand that the CO_2 balloon falls faster because it is less buoyant.

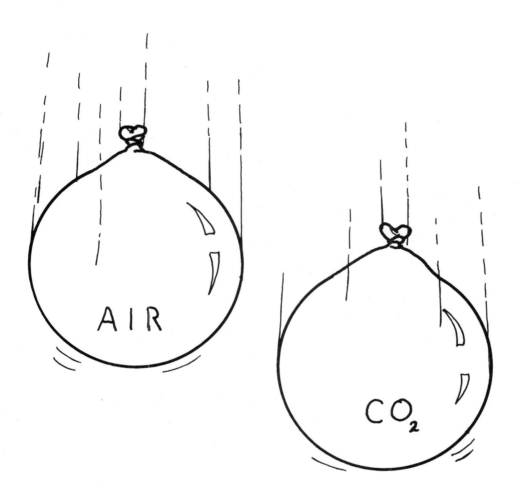

Name _____

Date _____

Presence of Starch in Food

Student Project 14

The iodine/starch test is a standard test commonly used by chemists. When iodine is put on a material containing starch, a dark blue-black reaction can be observed. Using an eyedropper, place one or two drops of iodine on each substance and note the results.

Food	Reaction
Potato Chip	
Potato	
Apple Slice	
Flour	
Carrot Slice	
Cracker	
Water	
Milk	
Sugarcane	
Onion Slice	
Cabbage Leaf	
Other_____	
_____	
_____	

The lima bean is the most nutritious member of the pea family.

GA1443

Cracker Tasting

Student Project 15

Crackers are made with flour. Flour contains lots of starch. Student Project 14 demonstrated that crackers contain starch. When you eat a cracker, the digestive process begins in the mouth. When you put a cracker in your mouth, the saliva produced in the salivary glands starts the process of digestion. Saliva contains the enzyme *ptyalin* which begins the digestion process by changing the starch in a cracker into a sugar.

Materials:

an unsalted cracker

Procedure:

Note the time; then place half of a cracker in your mouth and let it dissolve. DO NOT SWALLOW THE CRACKER! Note how long it takes for a sweet taste to be noticeable.

(A)   Beginning time   _____

(B)   Time cracker begins tasting sweet   _____

(B-A) Elapsed time   _____

Fill in the blanks below.

A _____, if left to dissolve in the mouth, will taste_____.

This is because saliva turns _____ into _____.

Algin, produced from giant kelp seaweed, is used in the production of toothpaste, aspirin, chocolate milk, ice cream, and other foods and drugs.

GA1443

Tasting Foods

Teacher/Student Project 5

Do you know that your nose knows about good taste? It may be new news about your nose knowing, but it's the truth...your nose knows. When you smell cookies baking, can't you almost taste them? Remember the last head cold you had? You probably had trouble tasting your food for several days. While this loss of a sense of taste may have a benefit when eating food you dislike, it does affect your favorite yummies too.

To check how much you rely on your nose to help you taste, taste the following foods with your nose tightly clamped closed and your eyes blindfolded.

Materials:
> blindfold
> various foods cut into $1/4$" (.6 cm) sections
>> (for example, onion, apple, potato, carrot, turnip, jicama, sugar beet, sugar-cane, beet, celery, cucumber)

Procedure:
> With your eyes and nose tightly closed, your teacher will place a food in your mouth. Without chewing, try to identify the food. After making your guess and having it recorded, unleash your sniffer and see if your nose knows the taste.

Person	Guess	Actual

Vision and Foods

Teacher/Student Project 6

The eyes play an important role in determining how a food will taste. Millions of dollars are invested in advertisements for frosty cold drinks, juicy hamburgers, crisp veggies, and yummy candies. But what would we think of blue burgers, pink French fries, purple orange juice, or green milk?

See for yourself how appetizing some drinks can be made by the addition of simple, nontasting food coloring.

Materials:

several common drinks
    (for example, milk, chocolate
    milk, orange and grapefruit
    juice, water, tomato juice,
    7-Up, and lemonade)

large, clear glass (for mixing)
food coloring
small, clear plastic cups

Procedure:

1. Mix food coloring with the various liquids to create a variety of colored drinks.

2. After each liquid is mixed, pour a small "taster" for students into their individual plastic cups.

Discussion Question:

What effect does a food's appearance have on its taste?

Magic Writing

Student Project 16

The fact that different materials oxidize or burn at different temperatures can be used to create a magic message. Oxidization is the process in which oxygen combines with something to change its appearance. A common example is found in the toaster. A slice of bread will combine with too much oxygen and get too brown–burned toast.

Citric acid from a lemon will oxidize or "burn" at a lower temperature than paper. This difference can be seen in the following experiment.

Materials:

paper	100-watt light bulb
lemon	toothpick or old, clean ink pen

Procedure:

Using the juice from a lemon, write a secret message on the paper. After the lemon juice dries, it will be invisible. To make the writing visible again, heat the paper carefully over the light bulb. The citric acid will oxidize at a lower temperature than the paper, thus revealing the writing. Be careful not to burn yourself while working near the hot light bulb.

Lightning bugs (fireflies) produce light by producing an enzyme, luciferase, that oxidizes a fat luciferin to produce a cool light.

Nature's Colors

Student Project 17

Nature abounds with colors. The pigments that give plants their varied colors can be studied in an interesting way.

Materials:

beakers, glasses or cups

colored flowers, leaves,
   grass or berries

alcohol

small stirring stick or spoon

Procedure:

1. Cut up the petals from a flower into small pieces.

2. Pour 1"-2" (2.54-5.08 cm) of alcohol into a clean beaker or glass and add the cut-up flower petals.

3. Use a stick or spoon to thoroughly smash the plant material until the pigments have colored the alcohol.

4. Place a 1" (2.54 cm) wide strip of white construction paper in the alcohol as illustrated.

5. Place the beaker or glass on a table, chalk rail, or in front of a bulletin board so the construction paper can be pinned or taped vertically.

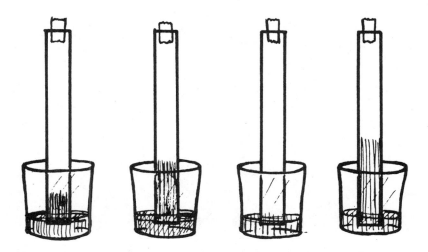

The flamingo gets its pink color from the algae and shrimp it eats.

37

Building a Terrarium

Student Project 18

To build a viable terrarium you need to remember some basic needs of plants. Plant roots need oxygen and too much water will kill most plants. Too little water and a plant's roots will dry out and die. A plant needs soil rich in nutrients, but overfertilizing a plant can be deadly to it as well. A plant needs sunlight, but a terrarium left in direct sunlight can generate temperatures high enough to kill plants. A plant in rich, well-drained soil, cared for with regard to warmth, sunlight, and occasional fertilizing can be a rewarding experience.

Use the diagram below to create an indoor garden.

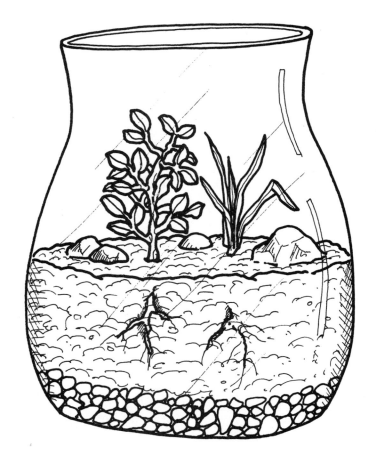

Biological Sciences–Animals

The study of animals in the classroom is best accomplished by the use of living specimens. Many animals make good classroom exhibits, and their proper care can be a good educational experience. It is important to make the students acutely aware of each animal's needs and the responsibility of a care giver to meet those needs.

Some animal populations, such as a mealworm colony, are simple to establish, easy to care for, and serve a dual purpose. Not only does it provide an interesting animal to study, it also is a ready food supply for larger animals such as frogs, salamanders, and lizards. Mealworms are usually obtainable at pet or feed stores.

To start your own mealworm colony, place 500 mealworms in a one-gallon jar or small aquarium and add wheat bran laced with cornmeal. Occasionally add a small piece of apple, potato, or carrot to add variety and moisture to their diet. The partial metamorphosis from larvae to adult will add to the students' understanding of life cycles.

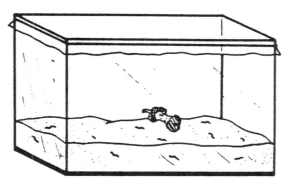

Teacher/Student Project 7

(**Note:** A healthy, large population of mealworms can also be used to clean skulls of small mammals and reptiles.)

To integrate math into your science program, mealworm races can focus the students' attention on speed, distance, and graphing, as well as animal location. Determining a mealworm's speed in miles per hour is a real math challenge.

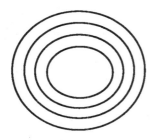

Awards can be found on pages 85 and 86 to present to the racers.

Student Project 19

GA1443

Graphing the speeds of different animals is a good math follow-up to the mealworm race.

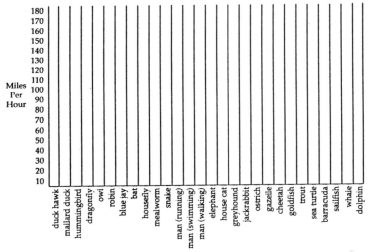

Student Project 20

If you have access to a mulberry tree, growing silkworms is a great springtime activity. Order silkworm eggs in early spring from a biological supply house. (See page 89.)

Teacher/Student Project 8

Studying the life cycle of the silkworm is a great way to study metamorphosis (Greek: meta = change + morphe = form; change in form). Caterpillars of other moths and butterflies as well as larvae transitions of mealworms can also be studied. The change of frog and toad "tadpoles" to adults are also good examples to study. The lowly fruit fly is another animal whose life cycle is able to be viewed in the classroom. ✆

Student Project 21   **Teacher/Student Project 9**

GA1443

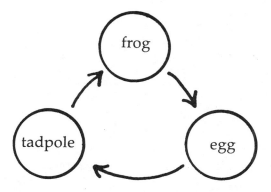

The study of frogs can be expanded to a study of pond biology. An emphasis on the interrelationship of organisms needs to be considered in this decision–where man fits into the picture of ecology of not only ponds but all of nature fits nicely into a discussion of interrelationships. Hatching frog eggs to tadpoles and raising them to adults is a great classroom or independent study project.

One does not have to live near a lake to study aquatic life dynamics. Any nearby stream, drainage ditch, or pond can provide material for an investigation. Seasonal considerations must be made and pond biology is a "natural" springtime activity.

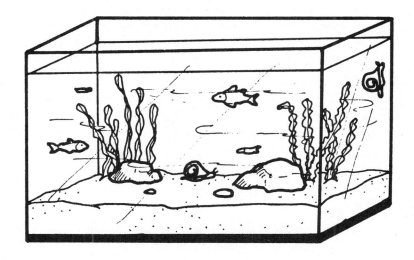

Teacher/Student Project 10

To indicate the dependence of larger animals upon smaller animals and plants as a food source, a superculture can be set up. With the aid of a microscope, the food chain at its lowest levels can be observed. Supercultures are always of keen interest to students because they allow them the thrill of discovery. Supercultures can be somewhat odiferous, but are well worth the olfactory inconvenience.

Teacher/Student Project 11

Supercultures can be a great place to "spin off" to health, hygiene, and germs. Germs, bacteria, and viruses are also part of the animal kingdom but are best generally avoided as a study aid at this level. A discussion of the number of germs on the hands and under the nails (in the millions) will have the whole class ready to "wash up" before lunch.

A $\frac{1}{2}$ -ounce snail can "pull" up to a pound in weight.

Mealworm Farm

Teacher/Student Project 7

Mealworms are an interesting insect to grow and observe. Their life cycle is dependent upon food supply, moisture, and temperature. The adult beetle mates and lays eggs. These eggs hatch into a larvae stage called mealworms. Shedding the shell several times as they grow, these mealworms metamorphose, or change form, into the adult beetle which starts the process all over.

To start a colony of mealworms you'll need:

1. mealworms (50-500 to start depending on your plans to use mealworms as a food supply for larger animals)

2. large, clean glass jar or small aquarium

3. a covering over the container to keep out ants and other mealworm eaters (cheese-cloth or screen)

4. one or two pounds (.45 or .90 kg) of bran (available at feed or pet stores; also available at some grocery stores but more expensive)

5. Add an apple core, potato, watermelon rind, etc., occasionally for moisture. Add together the ingredients, mealworms, bran and potato, apple, etc. Keep the colony in a warm (not hot) place. **No Direct Sunlight!** The area should preferably be darkened, but this is not a necessity. Then observe the different stages of development the critters go through. Use a hand lens to look for eggs and discover emerging mealworms. Depending on heat, the beetles will go through their changes in two to three months and continue as long as they have space, food, and moisture. (Don't overdo it with the apple cores. . .one every two to three weeks will be enough.)

43

GA1443

Name _____

Date _____

Mealworm Races

Student Project 19

On your mark. . . get set. . .go!

Select from your mealworm colony an active, energetic, speedy-looking mealworm. Give your racer a name and pep talk before entering him or her in the race. Past names of winners have included Flash, the Wonder Worm, Speedy I, Speedy II, Megafoot, Harriet, One Intrepid Steed, and Mr. Quick.

The racetrack is made of four concentric, equally spaced circles on a sheet of construction paper.

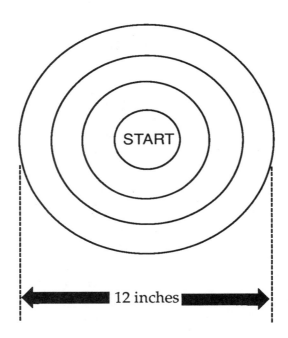

Race Rules:

Four or five students place their racing mealworms in the start circle and the first mealworm to reach the outside edge of the largest circle is the winner. Heats may be run to determine mealworms qualifying for the finals. The following chart can be used to determine your mealworm's speed.

44

A mealworm traveling the six inches to the outer edge (assuming a straight path was taken) had the following speed:

Mealworm's Name

_____

Owner's Name

_____

6 Inches In:	Speed
6 sec.	1/2 mph
9 sec.	1/3 mph
12 sec.	1/4 mph
15 sec.	1/5 mph
18 sec.	1/6 mph
21 sec.	1/7 mph
24 sec.	1/8 mph
27 sec.	1/9 mph
30 sec.	1/10 mph
33 sec.	1/11 mph
36 sec.	1/12 mph
39 sec.	1/13 mph
42 sec.	1/14 mph
45 sec.	1/15 mph
48 sec.	1/16 mph
51 sec.	1/17 mph
54 sec.	1/18 mph
57 sec.	1/19 mph
60 sec.	1/20 mph
63 sec.	1/21 mph
66 sec.	1/22 mph
69 sec.	1/23 mph
72 sec.	1/24 mph
75 sec.	1/25 mph

Time to travel 6 inches _____ (sec.)

Speed (See chart.) _____ miles per hour

If there are 5280 feet in 1 mile, complete the following:

$$\begin{array}{r} 5280 \\ \underline{\times\ 12} \end{array}$$ (feet in 1 mile)
(inches in 1 foot)

WORK SPACE

(A) _____ inches in 1 mile

Speed of your mealworm _____ mph

Denominator of your mealworm's speed
_____ (B)

Divide this number (B) into (A) to determine how many inches your mealworm could go in one hour. Divide this number by 12 (number of inches in a foot) to determine how many feet per hour your mealworm could go (assuming he didn't stop to rest).

GA1443

Having calculated how far in feet and inches your mealworm, if properly motivated, could go, find two places that are approximately this far apart and fill in below.

My mealworm, _____ , could travel
(name of mealworm)

from _____ to _____

in one hour.

Can you determine how long, at this rate, it would take your trusty mealworm to walk to your house?

Insects cannot close their eyes and must sleep with them open.

GA1443

Name _____

Date _____

Comparative Speeds

Student Project 20

From the speedy duck hawk, capable of hitting 180 mph in a dive, to your less than speedy mealworm, the animal kingdom is filled with creatures of different speeds. Finish the graph below.

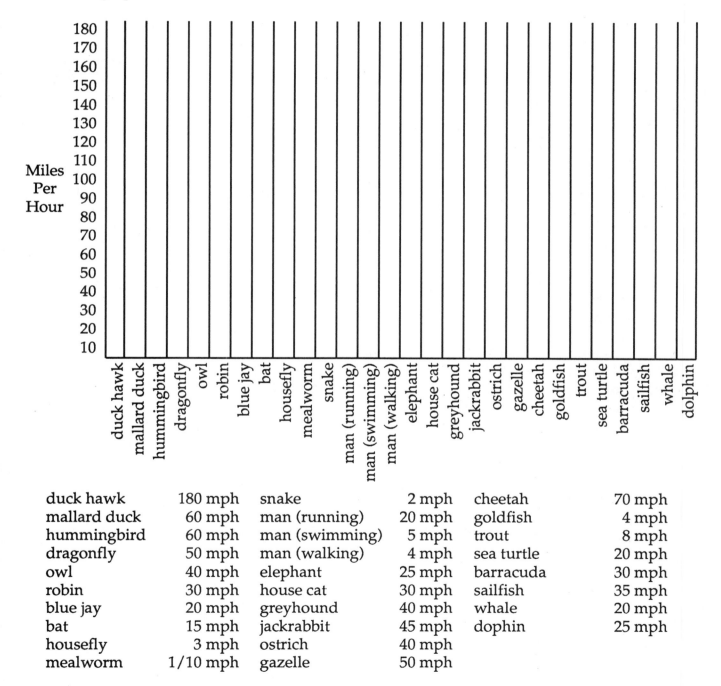

duck hawk	180 mph	snake	2 mph	cheetah	70 mph
mallard duck	60 mph	man (running)	20 mph	goldfish	4 mph
hummingbird	60 mph	man (swimming)	5 mph	trout	8 mph
dragonfly	50 mph	man (walking)	4 mph	sea turtle	20 mph
owl	40 mph	elephant	25 mph	barracuda	30 mph
robin	30 mph	house cat	30 mph	sailfish	35 mph
blue jay	20 mph	greyhound	40 mph	whale	20 mph
bat	15 mph	jackrabbit	45 mph	dophin	25 mph
housefly	3 mph	ostrich	40 mph		
mealworm	1/10 mph	gazelle	50 mph		

GA1443

Silkworm Ranching

Teacher/Student Project 8

Silk is a strong fiber used to make cloth. Discovered about 3000 years ago in China, the thread-like fibers are used today to make clothing, neckwear, curtains, and upholstery. Silk fiber comes from the cocoons spun by the caterpillars of a moth (Bombyx mori). Part of its scientific name comes from the scientific name of the mulberry tree (Morus) on which it feeds. Although several other animals, such as spiders and lace wings, can spin silk, it cannot be economically made into cloth. (Note: Because of its beauty, silk is often called the Queen of Fibers.)

The life cycle of the silk moth begins with the female laying between 300-500 eggs. About twenty days later, the eggs hatch into tiny silkworms. Silkworms have a terrific appetite and in about a month are seventy times their original size. Measuring about three inches (7.62 cm) in length when fully grown, the silkworm stops eating and spins a cocoon. The silk is produced in two glands near the silkworm's lower jaw. Spinning usually takes about three days and results in an egg-shaped cocoon encasing the silkworm.

Inside the cocoon, the worm changes into a pupa. The pupa metamorphoses (changes) into a moth in about three weeks. The moth emerges from the cocoon and mates, lays eggs, and the process repeats itself.

Silkworm Farming Directions

Materials:
>   clean, cardboard box
>   silkworm eggs
>   fresh mulberry leaves (must be provided daily)

Procedure:
>   Place the tiny silkworms on a supply of fresh mulberry leaves in a clean cardboard container. Keep the silkworms warm (not in direct sunlight!) and daily add fresh leaves. (A temporary, and only temporary, substitute can be orange or lettuce leaves.) Daily clean the container of unused, dry, or old leaves, removing carefully any silkworms attached. As the worms grow, their appetite increases and more leaves are needed.

After four or five weeks, the full-grown silkworms will start to spin cocoons. Place these cocoons in a box top or other shallow paper container. Approximately three weeks later the adult moths will enlarge, mate, and begin to lay eggs. These eggs can be saved (left on paper) and refrigerated for next year's use or allowed to hatch and continue the cycle. Good ranching!

GA1443

Silkworm Life Cycle

Student Project 21

Cut out the circles on the left, and paste them into the circles at the right in the correct order.

moth coming
out of cocoon

silkworm hatching
from egg

moths mating

silkworm spinning
cocoon

silkworm eating
mulberry leaves

completed silk
cocoon

moth laying eggs

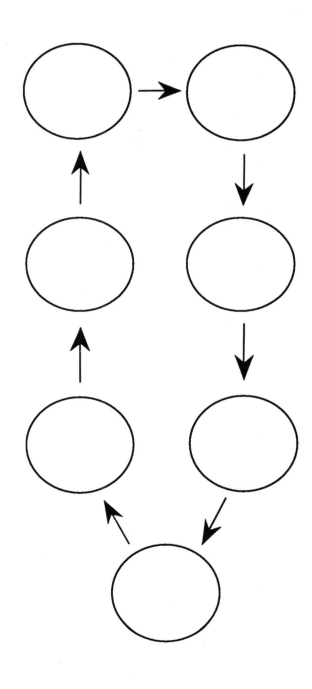

49

Growing Fruit Flies

Teacher/Student Project 9

The fruit fly is a small, easily raised little critter that will go out of its way to be caught. It is one of the most studied members of the animal kingdom, and because of its short life span and ease of care, it has been used extensively for genetic research.

Materials:

2-3 very ripe bananas
5 tbl. (75 ml) cornmeal
water
2 tbl. (30 ml) sugar

(overripe grapes, apples, pears, peaches, etc., can also be added if available)

Procedure:

Mash and mix the bananas, sugar, and cornmeal and add enough water to make a mixture the consistency of very thick syrup. Pour this mixture in two or three jars and place them in different areas. The areas you select should be protected from rain and direct sunlight but accessible to the outdoors (you may wish to observe one jar indoors). After three to four days, several fruit flies should be buzzing happily around your jar. When the fruit flies have been visiting the mixture for several days, cover the jars with cheesecloth, a window screen, or a clean cloth and observe. In a few days you should be able to observe the maggots and pupae of the fruit flies and even watch the new adults emerge. (Observe under a hand lens or biocular microscope.)

GA1443

Pond Biology

Teacher/Student Project 10

Visit a local "wild" water source (for example, pond, creek, river, or lake). Obtain four to five gallons (15.12 to 18.90 l) of pond water, some pond substrata, and any plants or animals you can. Add a crawfish or two, some snails and even a fish or two from your local pet store and you have a living study aid.

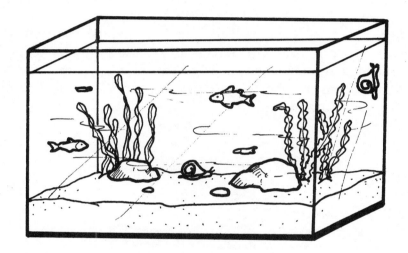

GA1443

Superculture

Teacher/Student Project 11

A superculture will provide the students with an opportunity to study the fascinating world of microbiology. Begin your superculture by obtaining a large, clean glass container that will hold about two gallons (7.56 l) of water. It is very important to obtain the water from an unchlorinated source. A semistagnant pool that has been standing for a while works great. To your water add some dried grass clippings, semidecomposed old leaves, and a handful of mud from a permanently damp spot. If a compost pile is available, add a handful from the bottom of the pile. A package of yeast can also be added if available.

Keep your superculture loosely covered. After a few days, a microscope slide with one drop of your superculture should reveal a multitude of paramecia, algae, ciliates and flagellates. Most of the "little critters" will be found at or near the bottom. Use a long pipette or soda straw (do not suck; cover the end with a finger) to get the bottom dwellers. Caution students about washing hands thoroughly with soap after touching the jar, slides, etc. A book on microbiology from the school or local library will help identify your "zoo in a jar." Good hunting!

GA1443

Chicken or duck egg incubation can be a good classroom focus for a science study. A primitive yet serviceable incubator can be made from an old aquarium, a glass quart jar, and an aquarium heater. Establishing a consistent temperature of about 103°F (39.4°C) will require a bit of trial and error but can be accomplished over a two or three-day period. The turning of the eggs is very important. Turning just twice a day can result in a 40 percent reduction in the rate of hatching. No turning can cut hatching by up to 85 percent. As hatching time approaches, a brooder box will need to be set up to receive the baby chicks or ducks.

Bricks or rocks may be added to help maintain a consistent temperature.

Teacher/Student Project 12

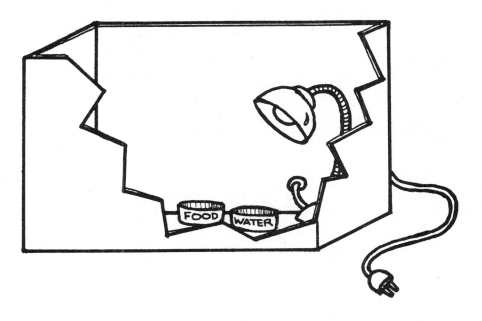

Teacher/Student Project 13

GA1443

The study of insects (entomology) is an interesting way to approach the biology of the students' environments. Include bees, ants, cockroaches, moths, fireflies, fleas, crickets, butterflies, ladybugs, walking sticks, and many more. The availability of creatures to study is almost limitless. Of the roughly one million different kinds of animals, roughly 900,000 are insects. Thousands of new insects are discovered every year.

It should be pointed out to the students that in addition to the enormous numbers of different kinds of insects, the numbers of individuals is staggering. It has been estimated that each square mile of land may contain as many insects as there are humans on the planet Earth.

Insects are a most unique group of animals. Most smell with their antennae while some taste with their feet. Some "hear" through their hairs while others have ears on their legs or the sides of their bodies. Having no lungs, most insects breathe through holes in their bodies, and although some have no eyes at all, others have as many as five eyes. Insects have no voices, but some make noises that can be heard at distances of up to a mile away.

Insects are a diverse group; however, they share some characteristics which allow them to be grouped together as members of the insect world. All insects have three body parts and six legs, and most have antennae.

Many students think that spiders are insects because of their size and general shape. Spiders are classified as arachnids and have two body parts, eight legs, and fangs. Compared to the nearly one million different kinds of insects, there are about 30,000 different kinds of spiders. An insect specimen collection can be started very simply with a small cardboard box, some straight pins, and common insects found locally. A "killing jar" can be made with a small glass jar containing a cotton ball soaked in alcohol. Use a small strip of paper to identify each specimen.

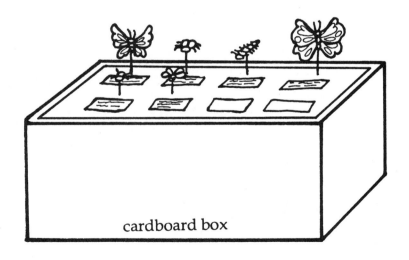

cardboard box

Teacher/Student Project 14

54

GA1443

Incubator

Teacher/Student Project 12

Materials:

10-gallon (37.8 l) aquarium
glass, metal, or wood aquarium cover
large glass jar (1 qt. [.95 l])
aquarium heater

thermometer
1-2 bricks (optional)
pie pan filled with water

Procedure:

Fill the jar with water and attach the aquarium heater to the top. This will serve as your heat source. Cover the aquarium with a piece of glass or other suitable material, leaving a small crack of $1/2$" (1.25 cm) for ventilation. Use the thermometer to monitor the temperature of the aquarium and regulate the aquarium heater until a constant temperature of 103°F (39.4°C) is achieved. A brick beneath the jar will help maintain a more constant temperature. Place a pan of water in the aquarium for humidity and add fertile eggs when a constant temperature has been maintained for two days. Mark the eggs with a pencil around the sides and turn them three or four times a day.

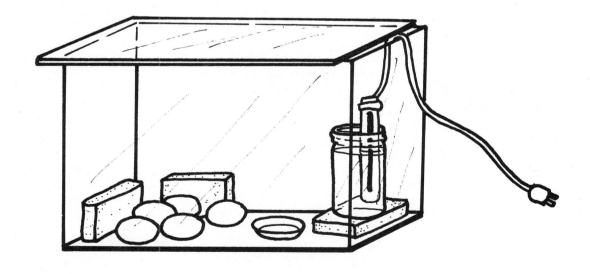

GA1443

Brooder

Teacher/Student Project 13

It is important to keep the newly hatched chicks or ducks warm and free from drafts. A satisfactory brooder can be made using a large cardboard box.

Materials:
>   cardboard box (approx. 2 ft. square [.18 sq. m])
>   reflector hood with 75-watt light bulb
>   shallow water dish
>   shallow food dish
>   baby chick mash
>   newspapers
>   thermometer

Procedure:
>   Line the bottom of a cardboard box with newspapers. Attach a reflector light to help heat the box. Try to keep the temperature around 100°F (37.7°C). Depending on the box size, weather conditions, etc., the light may have to be raised or lowered. Do not overheat the box. The baby chicks need to be able to get away from the light if it is too hot. Add a shallow food and water dish and enjoy your new pets.

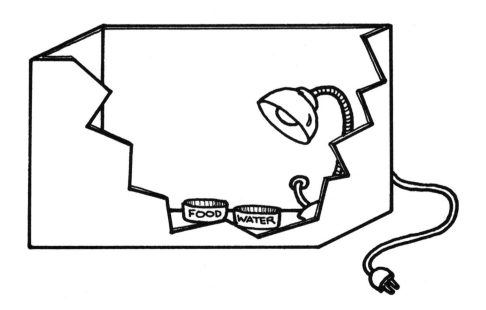

GA1443

Insect Collections

Teacher/Student Project 14

Materials:

cardboard box
construction paper
straight pins
small glass bottle with lid

alcohol
cotton balls
various insects
identification slips

Procedure:

Specimens can be killed by placing them in a glass bottle containing an alcohol-soaked cotton ball. Specimens can then be mounted on the cardboard box. Add name tags for identification.

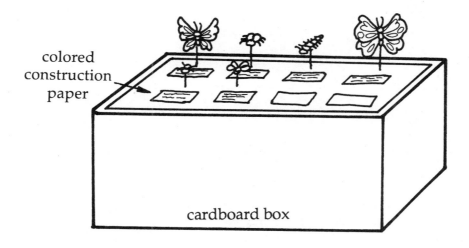

colored construction paper

cardboard box

GA1443

Once a constant temperature has been established and a dozen fertile eggs have been placed in the incubator, you may wish to further explore the embryo development. When opened and poured carefully into a shallow tray, the heartbeat of a three-day-old embryo can be seen. You may wish to repeat an egg opening several more times at three-day intervals to allow the students to observe the embryo's development.

A call to a local feed store will probably provide a source for fertile eggs as well as baby chick mash and answers to questions that may arise. Chicken eggs hatch in twenty-one days while duck eggs (depending on the species) take about twenty-eight days.

After stimulating the students' interest in birds, try a bird checklist to find the kinds of birds in your area. Awards can be given to the students identifying the most species of birds. A trip to the local library for some bird books or a visit from a local Audubon Society member may be used to extend the study.

Bird Checklist	
dove	___
pigeon	___
seagull	___
quail	___
sparrow	___
finch	___
thrush	___

Student Project 22

An additional project dealing with eggs is the egg drop contest. Students create a package, parachute, springs, etc., to protect an egg from a fall. The egg surviving the fall from the highest altitude is the winner. Awards for the winners can be found in the back of this book. Making Humpty Dumptys from the fresh eggs is also a great art extension for egg studies.

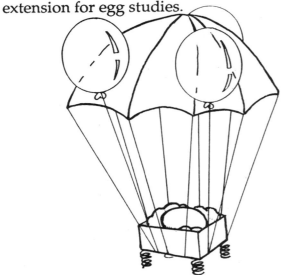

Student Project 23

Student Project 24

GA1443

A fun art project can be the making of name bugs.

  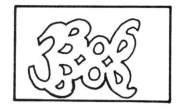

Student Project 25

A study of insect camouflage can be conducted in a grassy area and will give the students a good understanding of the use of camouflage in nature.

Camouflage Chart

Color of "Insect"	Number of Insects Found	Total Number of Insects of That Color	Percent of Insects Found (# insects found / total # insects of that color)
Green			
Red			
Blue			
Brown			
Tan			
White			
Black			

Student Project 26

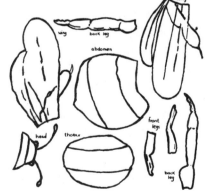

Student Project 27

A study in insect mobility can be explored with the study sheet provided. Also provided are two large cutouts of insect parts that can be cut out and pasted on construction paper to create a much enlarged insect to make an interesting bulletin board.

Insect Name	Type of Locomotion			
	Flying	Hopping	Swimming	Walking/Crawling
cricket				
housefly				
dragonfly				
caterpillar				
ladybug				
moth				
cockroach				
ant				
butterfly				
grasshopper				
flea				
termite				
bumblebee				

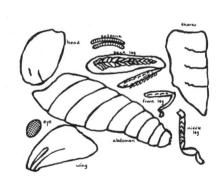

Student Project 28   **Student Project 29**   **Student Project 30**

The further study of insects could include any of the following: insect collages, reports on specific insects, microscopic investigations of insect parts, investigations on poisonous and harmful insects as well as man's benefits from insects, insect anatomy, migration, insect metamorphosis, and insect social orders.

GA1443

Bird Checklist

Student Project 22

Place a check mark beside those birds you identify in your community.

_____	1. duck		_____	26. kingfisher
_____	2. goose		_____	27. martin
_____	3. grouse		_____	28. meadowlark
_____	4. pheasant		_____	29. mockingbird
_____	5. quail		_____	30. nighthawk
_____	6. coot		_____	31. nuthatch
_____	7. crane		_____	32. pigeon
_____	8. killdeer		_____	33. raven
_____	9. swan		_____	34. roadrunner
_____	10. woodcock		_____	35. robin
_____	11. tern		_____	36. shrike
_____	12. gull		_____	37. swallow
_____	13. cockatoo		_____	38. swift
_____	14. parrot		_____	39. tanager
_____	15. oriole		_____	40. thrush
_____	16. blackbird		_____	41. warbler
_____	17. blue jay		_____	42. waxwing
_____	18. bluebird		_____	43. woodpecker
_____	19. canary		_____	44. wren
_____	20. cardinal		_____	45. _____
_____	21. crow		_____	46. _____
_____	22. dove		_____	47. _____
_____	23. sparrow		_____	48. _____
_____	24. finch		_____	49. _____
_____	25. grackle		_____	50. _____

There are over 8600 different species of birds in the world.

GA1443

Egg Drop Device Contest

Student Project 23

Construction Requirements:
Construct a device that will protect a raw (uncooked) egg from a fall. Anything goes. Good luck!

Testing:
Drop each device from several different heights until a sole survivor can be determined.

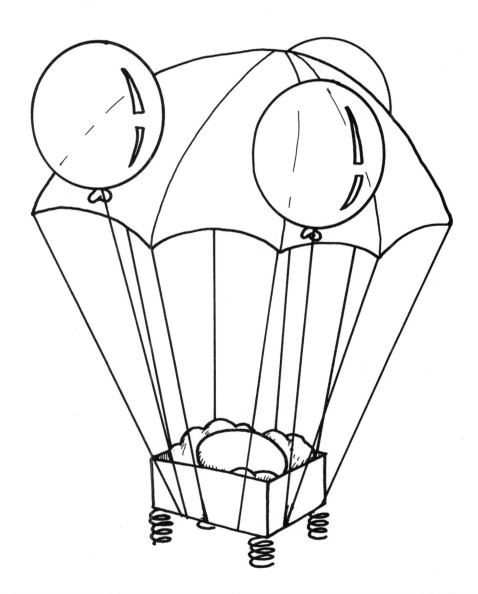

Light as a feather? A bird's feathers weigh more than its skeleton.

GA1443

Humpty Dumpty

Student Project 24

Materials:

1 egg per student
BB's or lead bird shot pellets
  (available at sporting goods stores)
white glue
candle

decorations
  (for example, yarn, construction paper, beads, etc.)
felt-tipped pens
small nail

Procedure:

Make a small nail hole at each end of an egg. Blow out the contents of the egg. (This will require some hard work.) After the egg has been emptied, rinse out the inside and blow out the excess water. Place 6-8 BB's or 10-15 lead bird shot pellets in the egg. Squeeze in 2-3 drops of glue and set upright to dry (about 24 hours). Use a drop of candle wax to seal both holes. Decorate.

The mako shark is the world's fastest shark, able to swim at speeds of over 40 miles per hour.

GA1443

Name Bugs

Student Project 25

Materials:

    2 sheets of different colored construction paper
    scissors
    paste
    crayons, colored markers

Procedure:

1. Fold one sheet of paper in half on the long side.

2. Write name in cursive with name touching folded edge.

3. Use a pencil to make a dotted line around the name.

4. Add other dotted lines for cutting. Taking care not to cut all of the fold away, cut on the dotted line.

5. Open name bug and paste on second sheet of construction paper, penciled side down.

6. Add additional artwork as desired.

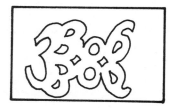

Name_____

Date_____

Insect Camouflage

Student Project 26

Materials:

    1 sheet each of various colored construction paper
    field or grassy area
    scissors

Procedure:

Cut about 1000 shapes of paper into insect-sized pieces. Each color needs to be equally represented. (Stacking the various colors of paper on top of each other and cutting or using a hole punch works well.) Record the total number of "bugs" made of each color.

Randomly scatter the "insects" in a meadow, field, or grass play yard without students watching. Allow the students to collect as many of the paper insects as possible in a five to ten-minute period. Have students total and record the number of insects found. Discuss the results with emphasis on how protective coloration benefits the survival of insects.

Camouflage Chart

Color of "Insect"	Number of Insects Found	Total Number of Insects of That Color	Percent of Insects Found $\left(\dfrac{\text{\# insects found}}{\text{total \# insects of that color}}\right)$
Green			
Red			
Blue			
Brown			
Tan			
White			
Black			

The archelon is an extinct marine turtle that had a shell over 12 feet long and weighed over 6000 pounds.

Creating an Insect

Student Project 27

Insects have three body parts (head, thorax, abdomen), six legs, antennae, and some have wings. Use three sections of an egg carton and other supplies to create your very own insect. When your creation is complete, you'll have an opportunity to hide your creation using the cryptic coloration you've employed. See if your insect is the last one found.

Materials:

egg cartons divided into sections of three
pipe cleaners
various colors of construction paper
toothpicks
yarn
other appropriate materials as available

Procedure:

After creating your own "insect," join your classmates in hiding your creatures. They cannot be buried; at least half of the insect must be visible. Hide your creations in a local park, meadow, etc. Be sure to set boundaries before anyone releases his or her insect.

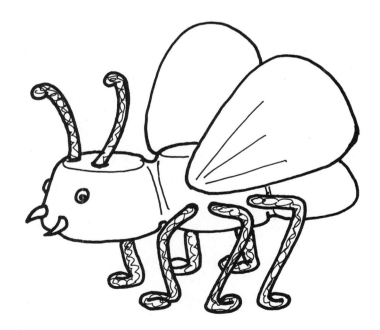

Insect Mobility

Student Project 28

Insect Name	Type of Locomotion			
	Flying	Hopping	Swimming	Walking/ Crawling
cricket				
housefly				
dragonfly				
caterpillar				
ladybug				
moth				
cockroach				
ant				
butterfly				
grasshopper				
flea				
termite				
bumblebee				

The sticky toe pads under the claws allow a fly to walk upside down on the ceiling.

GA1443

Grasshopper Anatomy

Student Project 29

Directions:
Cut out and build a grasshopper. Color and shade to add realism.

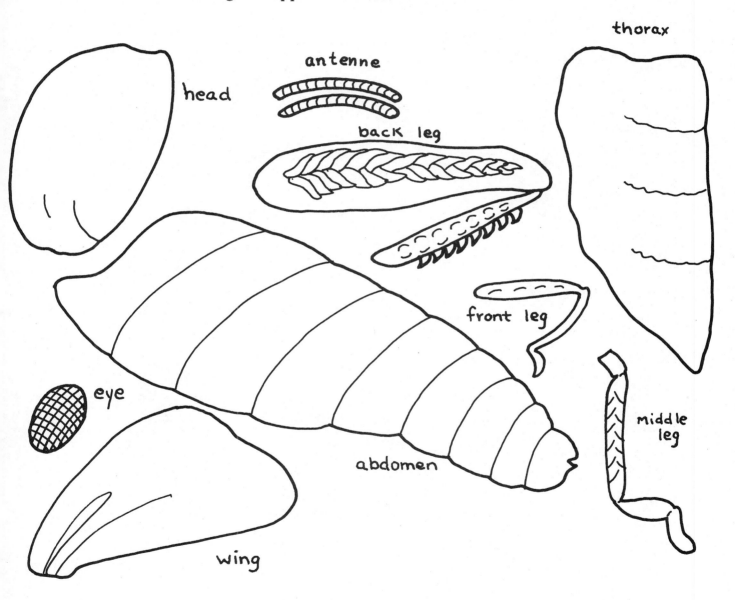

An ostrich egg is bigger than a grapefruit and as heavy as 4500 hummingbird eggs.

Honeybee Anatomy

Student Project 30

Directions:
Cut out and build a honeybee. Color and shade to add realism.

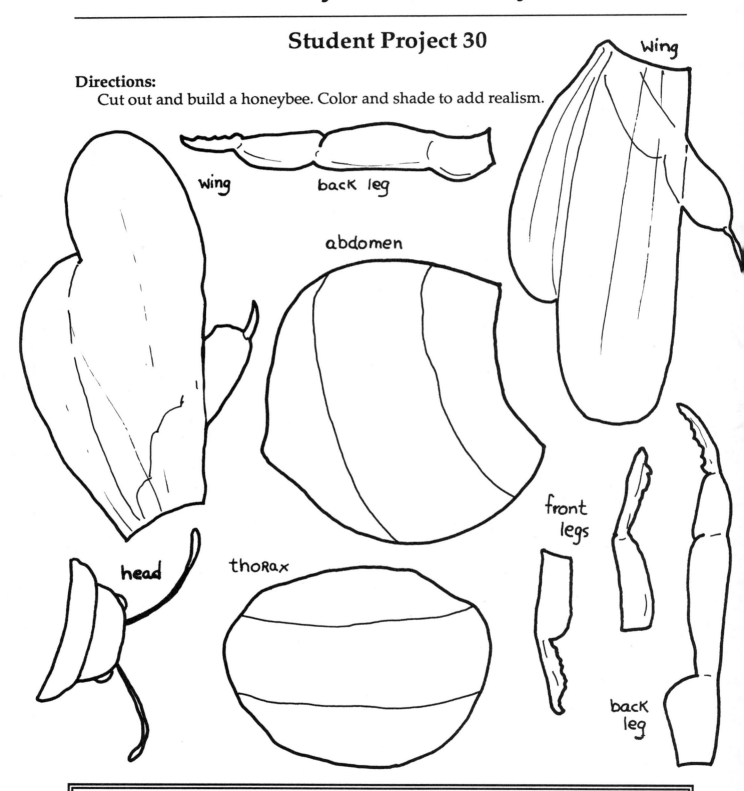

wing

back leg

wing

abdomen

front legs

head

thorax

back leg

A queen bee may lay 3000 eggs in a single day.

GA144

Animals with backbones are generally classified into five categories: fish, amphibians, reptiles, birds, and mammals. Having students categorize familiar animals will help them realize the characteristics that determine placement of the backboned animals into their respective categories.

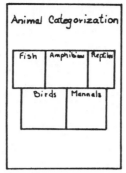

Student Project 31

Fish can be an interesting way to bring animals into the classroom. Easy-to-care-for goldfish can add a breath of animal life to the class. Setting up an aquarium with heater, aerator, filter, gravel, plants, and fish can help show the students the requirements and fun of pet ownership. By using seven, one-quart Mason jars; sand; snails; and elodea plants (available at pet stores), an interesting project can be devised to show the interdependence on the aquatic world.

| 6 plants | 5 plants 1 snail | 4 plants 2 snails | 3 plants 3 snails | 2 plants 4 snails | 1 plant 5 snails | 6 snails |

Teacher/Student Project 15
Student Project 32

Ink prints are another interesting way to further investigate the anatomy of fish. After each student has made his/her own print, a dissection of the fish will show the students that a fish is not "filled with goo" but has organs, each of which has a job to do.

Student Project 33

Holding a lizard roundup in the spring can provide an opportunity for the study of reptiles. After some practice with an old fishing pole and some monofilament fishing line tied into a slip noose, the lizard population in your community won't stand a chance.

Student Project 34

A terrarium can be set up to house the lizards caught during the roundup.

Teacher/Student Project 16

The study of bird beaks and their related foods can be accomplished in a unique auditorium project.

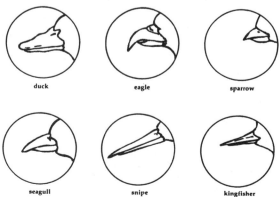

Student Project 35

Name _____

Date _____

Animal Categorization

Student Project 31

Directions:
Place the names listed below in their proper categories.

sturgeon	salamander	bear	robin	bass
warbler	shark	turtle	tuna	monkey
newt	crow	carp	whale	albatross
iguana	rattlesnake	frog	gecko	bat
lion	toad	tortoise	man	flounder
horse	kangaroo	elephant	hawk	eagle

Fish	Amphibians	Reptiles

Birds	Mammals

The African parrot and the myna bird of India are the best talkers.

GA1443

Aquatic Interdependence

Teacher/Student Project 15

Materials:

21 freshwater snails
21 freshwater elodea plants
7 one-quart jars with lids
sand
chlorine free water
 (Dechlorinating drops or water left to stand for 48 hours will work, but pond water is best.)

(Note: Both snails and plants are available at most pet stores.)

Procedure:

Place about 2" (5.08 cm) of sand (sandy soil from a pond will also work) in the jars and fill to within 1" (2.54 cm) of top with water. Carefully push the plant roots into the sand (a pair of chopsticks works great) and add the snails. Screw the lids on the jars and place them in a spot well lit but out of direct sunlight. Observe and record the results.

6 plants

5 plants
1 snail

4 plants
2 snails

3 plants
3 snails

2 plants
4 snails

1 plant
5 snails

6 snails

GA1443

Aquatic Interdependence

Student Project 32

Describe your observations of Teacher/Student Project 15. Include color of water, activity of snails, color of plants, etc. Answer at the beginning: Which jar do you believe will be the best balance? When you have determined which aquatic ecosystem is best balanced, give your reasons for the results.

Day	6 plants	5 plants 1 snail	4 plants 2 snails	3 plants 3 snails	2 plants 4 snails	1 plant 5 snails	6 snails
1							
3							
5							
7							
9							
11							
13							
15							
—							
—							
—							
—							
—							

GA1443

Fish Prints

Student Project 33

Materials:
1 small scaly fish (sunfish or rockfish)
sponge
ink
waxed paper
construction paper
rubber gloves

Procedure:
While wearing rubber gloves, wet, but do not saturate, the sponge with ink. Dab ink onto a dry, dead fish until it is "inked." Press the fish, ink-side down, onto the construction paper. (Some small experimentation on a large piece of butcher paper will perfect the technique.)

The fish prints make a great bulletin board.

The largest living animal in the world is the blue whale. It is over 100 feet long and weighs over 100 tons.

Lizard Roundup

Student Project 34

Lizards are an interesting reptile to study which can be collected in an interesting and fun way. Obtain a thin stick, 6-7 feet (1.82-2.13 m) long (a fishing pole works great), and to the end tie a slip noose, using four-pound test monofilament fishing line or strong thread.

The slip noose is made by first tying a tiny permanent loop in the line. This loop should be about the diameter of a pencil. Through this loop, slip the remaining line to create another loop that slips easily. Attach the other end of the line to your long pole and head out after your quarry.

Lizards are easiest to noose in the morning while they are basking in the sun on logs, fences, and rocks. Approach slowly and gently slide the slip noose over the lizard's head. In a short, quick motion, lift backwards and upwards from the lizard, snapping closed the noose.

Hold your captive in your hand and carefully loosen the noose. You can keep a lizard or two for closer observation in a properly prepared terrarium; or you may wish to apply one dot of bright fingernail polish to the back of the lizard, release him, and observe your marked specimen in its natural environment.

> *There are about 6000 different species of reptiles in the world.*

GA1443

Setting Up a Terrarium

Teacher/Student Project 16

Terrariums can be established in the classroom to fill various needs. As a home for lizards, a 10-gallon (37.8 l) aquarium covered with $1/4$" (.6 cm) galvanized hardware cloth works well. The substrata should be of clean, dry sand or kitty litter. "Hot rocks," available in most pet stores, can provide warmth; or a small, 60-watt bulb with a reflector can also be used. Add a rock or two, a small branch, and with a fresh supply of water and food your lizards should be happy.

Frogs need a larger water source as well as a substrata of moss. Allow places for "hiding" and your frogs will croak you their thanks.

Salamanders' requirements are similar to those of fish; however, some amphibians can have poisonous skins so be very careful about handling them.

Simple terrariums with only plants are easy to set up and require less attention than those with animals.

To create a plant-only terrarium, almost any plastic or glass container can be used. Cover the bottom of your selected container with thumb-size pebbles. Over the pebbles add 1" to 2" (2.54 to 5.08 cm) of charcoal (available at pet stores). Cover the charcoal with potting soil. Firmly pack the potting soil and when adding plants, be sure the roots are firmly packed into the soil. Monitor your watering closely to be sure you don't overwater. Use a "spritz" bottle to keep the leaves clean, and sparingly add one to two drops of plant fertilizer monthly.

Whether it be a single plant or an elaborate terrarium filled with scurrying critters, remember your responsibilities to provide all the necessary requirements for your plants and animals.

GA1443

Bird Beaks and Food

Student Project 35

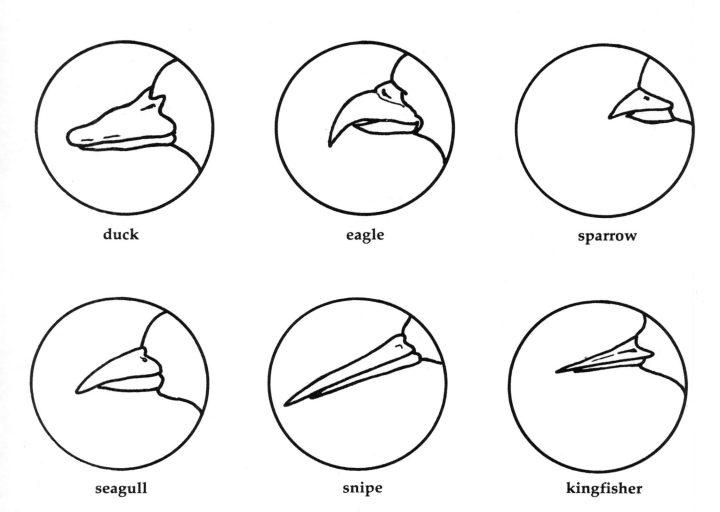

duck   eagle   sparrow

seagull   snipe   kingfisher

There is a great variety in bird beaks. This diversity demonstrates the great variation in the kinds of food birds eat. Some birds strain their food, some crack and eat seeds, some are almost completely insectivorous, while others catch large prey and tear the meat into bite-size portions.

To better understand the food gathering process and its relationship to different beak structures, complete the project on the following page.

GA1443

Materials:

Beaks: represented by plastic spoons, chopsticks, clothespins, knitting needles, tweezers, ice cream sticks, etc.

Food: represented by various small objects such as BB's, marbles, miniature marshmallows, dried beans or peas, dry macaroni, popcorn, 2" (5.08 cm) pieces of yarn, bottle caps, etc.

Mouth: paper cup

Procedure:

In a large, cleared area (the auditorium floor?) spread around the food on the floor. Each student is given a different kind of "beak" and using the beak, he is to pick up the food and place it in his cup. No sweeping of food into cups is allowed. After three to five minutes, have students spread out the food, trade beaks with another student and repeat. Repeat until students have tried each different "beak."

Discussion Questions:

1. Which bird beaks were easiest to use to gather food? Which were hardest?
2. Which foods could be gathered easiest by each beak?
3. What can you state about the relationship between a bird's beak and its food?

Birds can sleep without falling off their perches because of a tendon attached to each toe that locks the toes around the branch.

GA1443

Possible Plant Research Topics

1. Luther Burbank
2. George W. Carver
3. Carolus Linnaeus
4. Gregor Mendel
5. Charles Darwin
6. Flowers
7. Fruit
8. Vegetables
9. Algae
10. Bacteria
11. Seeds
12. Botany
13. Fertilizers
14. Chlorophyll
15. Hydrotropism
16. Photosynthesis
17. Hybrids
18. Grafting
19. Agriculture
20. Carnivorous Plants
21. Dutch Elm Disease
22. Leaves
23. Aquatic Plants
24. Kelp
25. Trees
26. Nuts
27. Adaptation
28. Agronomy
29. Horticulture
30. Marine Plants
31. Brophyte
32. Poisonous Plants
33. Mushrooms
34. Bark
35. Roots
36. Plant Diseases
37. Forestry
38. Paper Production
39. Rain Forests
40. Endangered Plants
41. Rose
42. Poppy
43. Snapdragon
44. Sunflower
45. Sweet Pea
46. Tulip
47. Zinnia
48. Marigold
49. Geranium
50. Daffodil

Possible Animal Research Topics

1. Ecology
2. Adaptation
3. Hibernation
4. Ornithology
5. Carnivorous
6. Mammals
7. Rabies
8. Ambergris
9. Incubation
10. Leather
11. Guano
12. Fur/Wool
13. Ivory
14. Pearls
15. Scorpions
16. Spiders
17. Tarantulas
18. Crabs
19. Lobsters
20. Frogs
21. Toads
22. Salamanders
23. Turtles
24. Alligators
25. Snakes
26. Lizards
27. Birds
28. Specific Bird Types
29. Weasels
30. Whales
31. Bears
32. Bats
33. Camels
34. Deer
35. Dogs
36. Cats
37. Coyotes
38. Wolves
39. Rodents
40. Instinct
41. Migration
42. Zoos
43. Wildlife Conservation
44. Charles Darwin
45. Animal Houses
46. Animals and Their Young
47. Animals' Ways of Protection
48. Camouflage
49. Animal Defenses
50. Animal Senses

GA1443

Plant Quiz

Name_____

Date _____

A. Write *true* or *false* in front of each statement.

1. _____ Plants are living organisms.

2. _____ Three healthy requirements for plants are food, nutrients, and sunlight.

3. _____ The process by which plants manufacture food is called photosynthesis.

4. _____ The force that directs plants to grow upward and their roots to grow downward is called hydrotropism.

5. _____ Roots provide a passageway for water and minerals to move into the plant.

6. _____ The green substance in plants is sugar.

7. _____ Evaporation is the process in which plants give off water vapor through their leaves and stems.

8. _____ Stamens and pistils are the reproductive organs of a flowering plant.

9. _____ Iodine turns the starch in plants red.

10. _____ Yeasts, small one-celled plants, are important in cooking because they produce carbon dioxide gas.

B. Fill in the missing letters to name the following plants.

11. T __ __ E __
12. E __ __ E R G __ __ __ N
13. __ A R __ __ T __ __ N
14. R __ __ E
15. T __ __ M __ T __
16. W A __ E R __ __ __ O N
17. O __ I O __
18. __ R A S __
19. D __ __ S Y
20. F __ R __

Animal Quiz

A. Write *true* or *false* in front of each statement.

1. _____ *Metamorphosi*s means "change of form."

2. _____ A spider is a type of insect.

3. _____ An embryo can only develop in a fertile egg.

4. _____ Snails are animals.

5. _____ Camouflage helps animals hide from predators.

6. _____ The five categories of vertebrates are animals, birds, reptiles, alligators, and fish.

7. _____ Plants and animals are interdependent on each other.

8. _____ Animals are always bigger than plants.

9. _____ All insects are harmful to man.

10. _____ Carnivores are meat eaters.

B. Fill in the missing letters to name the following animals.

11. B ___ A ___

12. H A ___ K

13. A ___ ___ E ___ O ___ E

14. S ___ ___ ___ K

15. F ___ X

16. ___ O ___ ___ A T

17. M A ___ ___ A ___ D

18. O ___ ___

19. R ___ T T ___ ___ S ___ ___ K E

20. G R ___ ___ ___ H O ___ ___ E ___

Plant Word Search

Find and circle the plant-related words listed below.

chlorophyll	nutrients	light	nucleus
photosynthesis	soil	cytoplasm	bark
stalk	leaf	cell	tropism
ovary	stem	yeast	germinate
enzyme	style	root	embryo
starch	pollen	stigmas	stamen
xylem			

P	C	H	L	O	R	O	P	H	Y	L	L	F	E	E	S	N
H	T	Q	E	F	N	S	J	E	A	E	Z	X	N	M	T	U
O	S	T	A	L	K	B	N	O	V	A	R	Y	Z	B	A	T
T	E	I	F	E	R	Q	U	M	N	T	H	L	Y	R	R	R
O	S	T	Y	L	E	O	C	O	P	S	T	E	M	Y	C	I
S	T	E	R	B	C	A	L	R	T	E	U	M	E	O	H	E
Y	A	T	J	A	O	H	E	N	H	N	P	O	L	L	E	N
N	M	A	Y	R	A	N	U	D	G	M	A	R	Y	W	E	T
T	E	N	T	K	T	O	S	T	I	G	M	A	S	H	B	S
H	N	I	Q	C	Y	T	O	P	L	A	S	M	U	T	I	O
E	N	M	C	K	B	O	R	X	W	J	O	U	N	O	F	I
S	T	R	O	P	I	S	M	M	P	O	F	V	I	O	E	L
I	R	E	D	K	A	T	Y	H	C	C	E	L	L	R	H	L
S	E	G	R	Y	E	A	S	T	Y	E	L	E	N	W	S	C

GA1443

Animal Word Search

Find and circle the animal-related words listed below.

beak	food	organ	bird
mealworm	superculture	brooder	insect
metamorphosis	cocoon	reptiles	egg
ecology	incubation	fish	nocturnal
embryo	aquarium	gestation	habitat
spider	camouflage	mobility	aquatic
terrarium	insectivorous	carnivorous	reproduction
silk	diurnal	nest	amphibian
mammal			

M	O	B	I	L	I	T	Y	B	I	N	S	E	C	T	E	V
H	D	M	E	T	A	M	O	R	P	H	O	S	I	S	E	R
A	I	Y	C	S	I	L	K	O	C	I	A	U	N	N	C	G
B	U	C	O	C	O	O	N	O	A	N	Q	P	C	O	A	O
I	R	N	L	O	B	I	R	D	R	S	U	E	U	C	M	D
T	N	E	O	A	B	Y	O	E	N	E	A	R	B	T	O	D
A	A	S	G	O	E	S	F	R	I	C	T	C	A	U	U	I
T	L	T	Y	N	E	N	M	W	V	T	I	U	T	R	F	I
A	M	P	H	I	B	I	A	N	O	I	C	L	I	N	L	G
Q	E	E	S	T	E	H	M	T	R	V	I	T	O	A	A	E
U	A	M	F	I	S	H	M	M	O	O	E	U	N	L	G	S
A	L	B	X	S	D	B	A	L	U	R	P	R	L	R	E	T
R	W	R	E	P	T	I	L	E	S	O	N	E	G	G	C	A
I	O	Y	P	I	O	R	G	A	N	U	W	A	Q	U	J	T
U	R	O	N	D	B	E	A	K	G	S	P	I	D	E	R	I
M	M	I	T	E	R	R	A	R	I	U	M	P	U	Y	K	O
F	O	O	D	R	E	P	R	O	D	U	C	T	I	O	N	N

GA1443

Awards

3rd Place
Egg Drop
Device
Presented to

_____

2nd Place
Egg Drop
Device
Presented to

_____

Presented to

_____

F
I
R
S
T

EGG DROP
DEVICE

Mealworm
Races
2nd Place
Presented to

_____

Mealworm
Races
1st Place
Presented to

_____

Mealworm
Races
3rd Place
Presented to

_____

SCIENCE
AWARD

presented to

_____

for

_____

date_____

signed_____

Graph Paper

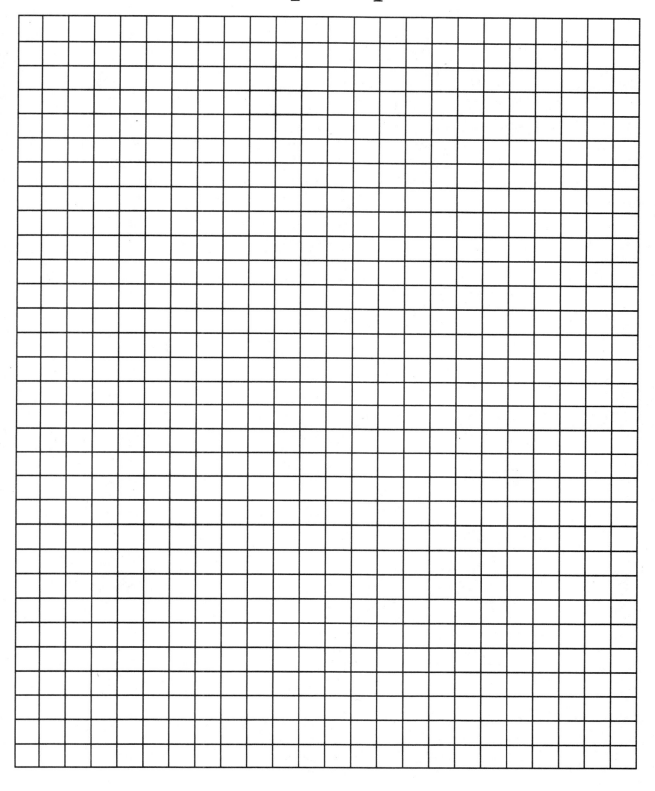

Dear Parents,

Our class is currently studying science, and we are in need of a number of materials. If it is possible, could you contribute some of the necessary items listed below? Your help with your child's projects is appreciated. Please take this opportunity to discuss with your child the science projects we are completing at school. Thank you for your support.

Sincerely,

We need the following items:

_____

_____

_____

_____

_____

_____

_____

_____

Science Supply Companies

Carolina Biological Supply
1400 N. Goodman St.
Rochester, NY 14602

Central Scientific Co.
11222 Melrose Ave.
Franklin Park, IL 60131

Delta Education
P.O. Box M
Nashua, NH 03061

Edmund Scientific Co.
101 E. Glouster Pike
Barrington, NJ 08007

Este Industries (Rocketry)
Dept. 1695
Penrose, CA 81240

Fisher Scientific Company
Educational Materials Div.
4901 W. LeMoyne St.
Chicago, IL 60651

Frey Scientific Co.
Hickory Ln.
Mansfield, OH 44905

NASCO
901 Janesville Ave.
Ft. Atkinson, WI 53538

NASCO West
P.O. Box 3837
Modesto, CA 95352

Turtox, Inc.
5000 W. 128th Place
Alsip, IL 60658

Wards Natural Science
5100 W. Henrietta Rd.
P.O. Box 92912
Rochester, NY 14692

Other Science-Related Addresses

The Good Apple Newspaper
Good Apple
1204 Buchanan St., Box 299
Carthage, IL 62321-0299

National Aeronautic and Space
  Administration (NASA)
Educational Branch
Washington, D.C. 20546

National Geographic Society
17th and M Streets NW
Washington, D.C. 20036

National Science Teachers Assoc.
1742 Connecticut Ave. NW
Washington, D.C. 20009

National Wildlife Federation
1412 16th St. NW
Washington, D.C. 20036

GA1443

Answer Key

Life Cycle of a Flowering Plant, page 24

6	The seed falls to the ground.
1	Pollen is produced on the stamen.
8	The embryo grows into a new plant.
2	Pollen is transported by insects, wind, etc., to the stigma.
5	A seed coat is formed around the embryo to protect it.
7	Moisture causes the seed coat to swell and open.
3	Pollen travels down the pistil to the ovary.
4	Fertilization produces a plant embryo.

Silkworm Life Cycle, page 49

Moth coming out of cocoon
Moths mating
Moth laying eggs
Silkworm hatching from egg
Silkworm eating mulberry leaves
Silkworm spinning cocoon
Completed silk cocoon

Insect Mobility, page 66

Flying–housefly, dragonfly, ladybug, moth, ants (some), butterfly, grasshopper, termites (some), bumblebee
Hopping–cricket, grasshopper, flea
Swimming–dragonfly (larva)
Walking/Crawling–all

Animal Categorization, page 71

Fish–sturgeon, shark, carp, tuna, bass, flounder
Amphibians–newt, salamander, toad, frog
Reptiles–iguana, rattlesnake, turtle, tortoise, gecko
Birds–warbler, crow, robin, hawk, albatross, eagle
Mammals–lion, horse, kangaroo, bear, elephant, whale, man, monkey, bat

Plant Quiz, page 81

1. true		11.	tree
2. false		12.	evergreen
3. true		13.	carnation
4. false		14.	rose
5. true		15.	tomato
6. false		16.	watermelon
7. false		17.	onion
8. true		18.	grass
9. false		19.	daisy
10. true		20.	fern

Animal Quiz, page 82

1. true		11.	bear
2. false		12.	hawk
3. true		13.	antelope
4. true		14.	skunk
5. true		15.	fox
6. false		16.	bobcat
7. true		17.	mallard
8. false		18.	owl
9. false		19.	rattlesnake
10. true		20.	grasshopper

Plant Word Search, page 83

Animal Word Search, page 84

GA1443